GREAT MEN & WOMEN of the BIBLE

Illustrations by
HEMESH ALLES

Compiled from *Bible People Quiz Book*
by **ERMA REYNOLDS**

*I*n ancient times, Solomon's Hebrew name, Shelomo, meant peace (*shalom*). Today, the name Solomon is synonymous for wisdom.

Accusers

Answers on page 84

1. Who accused his brothers of being spies?

2. What king accused his servants of conspiring against him?

3. Who accused Paul of polluting the temple?

4. What punishment was meted out to those who accused Daniel to Darius?

5. In which of Jesus' parables did a rich man accuse his accountant of stealing?

6. What tradesman accused Paul of hurting the sale of handcrafted goods?

7. What captain of the guard accused Jeremiah of defecting to the Chaldeans?

8. Who accused Moses and Aaron of exalting themselves above God's assembly?

9. What sect accused the disciples of law-breaking by harvesting grain on the Sabbath?

10. Who accused Naboth of blasphemy and had him stoned?

Angry People

Answers on page 84

1. Who was hot with anger when he left the presence of a stubborn king?

2. What soldier became angry because his young brother left sheep-tending to come to a battle site?

3. What man became so angry he cut a yoke of oxen into pieces?

4. What king became angry with three men and had them thrown into a fiery furnace?

5. Who became angry because God paid more attention to his brother than to him?

6. Who became angry with his mule and beat it with a stick?

7. What king left a banquet in a rage and went into the palace garden?

8. Who became so angry with his father he left the dinner table without eating?

Authors

Answers on page 84

1. Who is the first author to be mentioned in the Bible?

2. Who was told in a vision that what he saw he was to write in a book?

3. What preacher in a synagogue was handed a book written by the prophet Isaiah to read?

4. Who said his tongue was "the pen of a ready writer"?

5. Which author gave a copy of his book to a man, told him to tie a stone to it, and throw it into a river?

6. Who wished his words could be written and then printed in a book?

7. Who was the author of 3,000 proverbs?

8. Who wrote about the rights and duties of a kingdom and laid the book before God?

9. Who was the author of the Old Testament book that contains only one chapter?

10. What prophet wrote some of Solomon's biography?

Q

Babies

Answers on page 84

1. What baby was adopted by a princess?

2. What baby's weaning was celebrated with a great feast?

3. What baby's nurse was his mother?

4. What baby's nurse was his grandmother?

5. What twin baby boy was born grasping his brother's heel?

6. What baby was given a name by his dying mother, but had it changed by his father?

7. Who wished he had died when he was a baby?

8. Who was the first baby born on earth?

9. What baby's birth was announced by angels?

10. What baby was given in answer to a prayer?

The earliest Bibles, handwritten on scrolls, contained no vowels, punctuation, verses or chapters. In order to understand the text, readers had to provide these themselves.

Beautiful People

Answers on page 84

1. What king wanted to show off his queen's beauty to banquet guests?

2. Who was beautiful "from the sole of his foot even to the crown of his head"?

3. What young shepherd was handsome and had ruddy cheeks?

4. Whose daughters were said to be the fairest in the land?

5. What girl was chosen to be queen as the result of a beauty contest?

6. What beautiful girl filled a pitcher at a well and gave a stranger a drink?

7. Who was the most handsome man in Israel, a head and shoulders taller than anyone else?

8. What beautiful woman caught the eye of a king as he strolled on a palace roof?

9. What slave was described as being "a goodly person, and well favored"?

10. What girl was so graceful and beautiful, a man was willing to work seven years to get her for his wife?

Q

Bereaved People

Answers on page 84

1. What bereaved father, whose two sons had been killed by fire, was forbidden to mourn for them?

2. What woman, whose husband and two sons had died, changed her name to one that meant "bitter"?

3. What prophet was instructed by God not to weep for his dead wife?

4. What bereaved son asked permission of a king to return his father's body to Canaan?

5. What bereaved husband purchased a cave for his wife's burial place?

6. What man, when told his 10 sons and daughters had been killed, shaved his head, tore his mantle, and fell to the ground?

7. What bereaved king mourned for his dead son, wishing he could have died in his place?

8. What bereaved father, whose little daughter had died, was told by Jesus, "Weep not; she is not dead but sleepeth"?

9. What bereaved husband set a pillar upon his wife's grave that is still there today?

Blessers

Answers on page 85

Each person listed in the left-hand column gave a blessing to a person, or persons, listed at the right. See if you can match them.

1. Isaac   ——— a. Mary and Joseph

2. Joshua   ——— b. Elkanah and his wife

3. Laban   ——— c. Children of Israel

4. Melchizedek ——— d. Caleb

5. David   ——— e. Jael

6. Moses   ——— f. Pharaoh

7. Simeon   ——— g. Jacob

8. Eli   ——— h. Sons and daughters

9. Jacob   ——— i. Barzillai

10. Deborah   ——— j. Abram

Contrary to popular belief, animals did not enter Noah's Ark two by two. Noah was told by God to take seven pairs of clean animals – those suitable for eating according to Hebrew dietary laws. Noah was also told to take one pair of all unclean animals and seven pairs of birds.

Q

Blind People

Answers on page 85

This quiz is about Scripture people who had eye problems. Pick the correct name from the choice of three.

1. What Ammonite king threatened to put out the right eye of men he defeated?
(a) **Nahash**
(b) **Nahamani**
(c) **Nahari**

2. What blind prophet was visited by a woman in disguise?
(a) **Ahaziah**
(b) **Abijah**
(c) **Ahijah**

3. When surrounded by an enemy, who prayed to God to strike them with blindness?
(a) **Elijah**
(b) **Elishaphat**
(c) **Elisha**

4. What sorcerer became blind as punishment for evil doings?
(a) **Elymas**
(b) **Simon Magus**
(c) **Witch of Endor**

5. Who saw two angels strike with blindness a group of men who were trying to break into his house?
(a) **Job**
(b) **Lot**
(c) **Hod**

6. What half-blind father was deceived by his son?
(a) **Eli**
(b) **Jacob**
(c) **Isaac**

7. What king, overtaken by an enemy army, had his eyes put out?
(a) **Zedekiah**
(b) **Zechariah**
(c) **Zerahiah**

8. What blind beggar had his eyesight restored by Jesus?
(a) **Barabbas**
(b) **Barnabas**
(c) **Bartimaeus**

Boys

Answers on page 85

1. What five-year-old boy was dropped by his nurse and lamed for life?

2. What boy had a city named for him by his father?

3. What boy carried wood to an altar to burn himself as a sacrificial offering?

4. What 12-year-old boy astounded temple priests with his intelligence?

5. What teenage boy was given a coat of variegated colors?

6. What two boys were taken to visit their dying grandfather?

7. What boy had a coat made for him each year by his mother?

8. What boy was only seven years old when he became king of Judah?

9. What dead boy, after receiving attention from Elisha, sneezed seven times and opened his eyes?

10. What boy, banished into the wilderness with his mother, almost died of thirst?

*T*he story of how God helped Joseph rise to power in Egypt after his brothers sold him into slavery has been the subject of many plays. The full story is in the Book of Genesis, chapters 37-46.

Brothers

Answers on page 85

Match the brother in the right-hand column
to the brother described on the left.

1. Solomon passed a death
sentence on to his brother. _____ a. Andrew

2. Abihu and this brother
were killed because they
offered strange fire to God. _____ b. Jacob

3. Seth had this murderer
for a brother. _____ c. James

4. Aaron acted as a
mouthpiece for this
brother. _____ d. Nadab

5. Peter and this brother
were fishermen. _____ e. David

6. Esau hated this brother
because he stole his
blessing. _____ f. Adonijah

7. Eliab rebuked this
brother for leaving sheep
unattended. _____ g. Simeon

8. John and this brother
discontinued mending
nets to follow Jesus. _____ h. Moses

9. Judah asked this brother
to help him fight
Canaanites. _____ i. Cain

15

Q

Builders

Answers on page 85

1. Who bought a hill and built a city on it?

2. Who built a house and booths for his cattle?

3. Who built fortified towers in Jerusalem?

4. Who said, "As a wise master builder I have laid the foundation, and another buildeth thereon"?

5. What divinely inspired craftsman built much of a Tabernacle?

6. Who built cities in mountains, and castles and towers in forests?

7. Who was the first shipbuilder?

8. What king was an expert in the building of waterworks?

In biblical times, synagogues were to be built on the highest point of the town; any buildings higher than the synagogue were to be destroyed. To get around this rule, many synagogues put a pole on the roof.

Business People

Answers on page 85

1. Who had extensive business dealings in grain?

2. Who went in the tent-making business with a man and wife team?

3. What prophet set up a widow in the oil business?

4. What woman was a success in the purple-dyed cloth trade?

5. What two kings went into shipbuilding together?

6. What silversmith claimed that because of Paul the sales volume of silver shrines was declining?

7. What prophet gave a comprehensive inventory of the exports and imports of Tyre?

8. What tax collector abandoned his business to follow Jesus?

9. What king was in the lumber business?

10. What king engaged in the business of buying and selling linen yarn?

Q

Buyers

Answers on page 86

The people listed in the left-hand column bought
one of the items listed on the right.
See if you can match them.

1. Potiphar ———— a. Cave for
burial use

2. Abraham ———— b. Land of Egypt

3. David ———— c. Wife

4. Joseph ———— d. Fine linen

5. Chief Priests ———— e. Bond servant

6. Boaz ———— f. Parcel of a field

7. Joseph of ———— g. Threshing floor
Arimathaea and oxen

8. Jacob ———— h. Hill of Samaria

9. Omri ———— i. Sweet spices

10. Mary Magdalene, ———— j. Potters field
Mary, Salome

Q

Captains

Answers on page 86

1. What captain of the host was a leper?

2. Who was David's chief captain that killed 800 men in a single battle?

3. What captain was murdered by a woman?

4. This first cousin of King Saul was also captain of his boat.

5. Who was the Roman captain who rescued Paul from Jerusalem Jews?

6. Who was the captain of the guard who bought Joseph?

7. What "mighty man of valour" was asked by the elders of Gilead, "Come, and be our captain, that we may fight with the children of Ammon"?

8. What refugee became captain of about 400 men?

9. What relative of David was appointed to be captain of the host in place of Joab?

10. What captain of the guard burned all the houses in Jerusalem when that city was taken?

Q

Answers on page 86

1. What man, taken captive by enemy kings, was rescued by his uncle?

2. What king, after being in captivity for 37 years, was released from prison and given a daily allowance of food for his lifetime?

3. What captive prophet mingled with other captives by the river Chebar?

4. What captive interpreted a king's dreams so well he was put in charge of a nationwide farm program?

5. At Babylon, what young captive of good birth was selected as a trainee for state service?

6. What captive king had his eyes put out and then was imprisoned?

7. What group of captives hung their harps on willow trees?

8. What king was taken captive by Nebuchadnezzar and deported to Babylon along with his mother, wives and officers?

9. Which book of the Bible gives the story of exiles returned to their own land again after years of captivity?

10. What Jewish captive was advanced to a high position in King Ahasuerus' kingdom?

Cattlemen

Answers on page 86

1. Who plowed with 12 pair of oxen?

2. What two men helped each other find pasture land for their cattle?

3. Who had thousands of his cattle and camels stolen?

4. Who made booths for his cattle?

5. What two cattlemen had to break up their partnership because of trouble between their herdsmen?

6. What prophet was a herdsman?

7. Who owned so many cattle that the Philistines became envious and they stopped up his wells?

8. What cattleman used his son-in-law as hired help to care for his herds?

9. Who was Saul's chief herdsman?

10. Who was the first of the cattlemen?

Q

Each person listed at the left hid something that is mentioned in the right-hand column. Match each concealer with the item hid.

1. Jochebed

_____ a. Battle spoils under a tent

2. Obadiah

_____ b. Idols in a bag

3. Jeremiah

_____ c. Baby by a riverside

4. Jacob

_____ d. Little prince in a temple storeroom

5. Moses

_____ e. Money in the earth

6. Rahab

_____ f. Body in sand

7. Servant in a parable

_____ g. Earrings under an oak tree

8. Achan

_____ h. One hundred prophets in caves

9. Rachel

_____ i. Two spies on a housetop

10. Jehosheba

_____ j. Stones in clay near a palace

Conspirators

Answers on page 87

Match the conspirator(s) listed on the
left with the person plotted against,
listed on the right.

1. Absalom	—— a. Elah
2. Servants	—— b. Joseph
3. Delilah	—— c. David
4. Gaal	—— d. Jesus
5. Jews	—— e. Joash
6. Jehu	—— f. Abimelech
7. Brothers	—— g. Samson
8. Ahimelech	—— h. Joram
9. Pharisees	—— i. Paul
10. Zimri	—— j. Saul

Solomon had more women in his life than anyone else mentioned in the Bible – 700 wives, plus 300 concubines (female slaves). Many of his marriages were political. Solomon accepted the daughters of foreign kings in exchange for promises of peace.

Converts

Answers on page 87

1. What man, who suddenly became blind, became a convert when he regained his sight?

2. On the day of Pentecost, how many people were converted?

3. What Roman centurion was converted by Peter?

4. Who converted an Ethiopian eunuch?

5. Who was told he would become a convert after meeting a band of prophets playing musical instruments?

6. What sorcerer became a convert?

7. What king recovering from insanity became a convert?

8. What "seller of purple" became a convert?

9. To which of his disciples did Jesus say, "But I have prayed for thee, that thy faith fail not; and when thou art converted, strengthen thy brethren"?

10. What proconsul became a convert after seeing a sorcerer punished with blindness?

Courageous People

Answers on page 87

Listed in the left-hand column are some courageous people. Match each person with his instance of bravery listed at the right.

1. Gideon   ____ a. Persisted in praying, even though it meant being thrown to lions.

2. Aaron   ____ b. Dared to ask Pilate for Jesus' body.

3. David   ____ c. During a battle in which he was deserted by fellow soldiers, he alone beat back the enemy.

4. Benaiah   ____ d. During a plague he dared to mingle with the stricken people, to make atonement for them with God.

5. Daniel   ____ e. Refused to run from danger and take refuge in a temple.

6. Joseph of Arimathaea   ____ f. Attacked a vast army with only 300 men.

7. Nehemiah   ____ g. Dared to face an enemy giant, armed with only a sling and staff.

8. Shammah   ____ h. Killed two lion-like men, a lion and Egyptian warrior.

Q

Covenanters

Answers on page 87

In the left-hand column are people who made
a covenant. At the right are articles, or
procedures, used to ratify the covenant.
See if you can match them.

1. Solomon – Hiram   ____ a. Rainbow

2. Hannah – God   ____ b. Gift of gold and silver

3. Asa – Benhadad   ____ c. Loss of right eyes

4. Rahab – Spies   ____ d. Child whose hair would never be cut

5. Abraham – Abimelech   ____ e. Food for a household

6. Judas Iscariot – Chief priests   ____ f. Robe, sword, bow, girdle

7. Jonathan – David   ____ g. Ewe lambs

8. Nahash – Jabeshnites   ____ h. Pile of stones

9. Noah – God   ____ i. Thirty pieces of silver

10. Laban – Jacob   ____ j. Scarlet cord

Covetous People

Answers on page 87

1. Who coveted spoils taken from an enemy?

2. Who coveted a vineyard?

3. Who said, "I have coveted no man's silver, or gold, or apparel"?

4. What servant coveted gifts his master had refused?

5. Who coveted "the wages of unrighteousness"?

6. What former sorcerer coveted the gift of the Holy Ghost?

7. What sect did Jesus denounce as being covetous?

8. What governor of Judaea coveted bribe money?

9. Who coveted fruit?

10. Who coveted money received from selling property?

*O*ne of the most famous stories in the Bible is that of David and Goliath. David's killing of the giant is recognized as a symbol of good over evil. (I Sam., chapter 17)

Cowards

Answers on page 88

Match the cowards in the left-hand column
with their particular demonstration of
cowardice listed at the right.

1. Pilate   _____ a. He proved to be a coward by yielding to a crowd that wanted him to make them an idol.

2. Adam   _____ b. They showed a cowardly streak during a storm at sea.

3. Israelites   _____ c. He was afraid to admit he knew Jesus.

4. Aaron   _____ d. He chose the night time to destroy an idolatrous altar, afraid of the consequences if he was found out.

5. Disciples   _____ e. Cowardice showed up when a giant appeared.

6. Abraham   _____ f. Fearful of a crowd, this coward condemned an innocent man to death.

7. Peter   _____ g. This cowardly husband shifted responsibility for disobedience upon his wife.

8. Gideon   _____ h. Fearful of being killed by Egyptians, he told his wife to pretend she was his sister.

Criminals

Answers on page 88

Match the people listed in the left-hand column with their crime listed at the right.

1. Ehud   _____ a. Kidnapping

2. Samson   _____ b. Theft

3. Gibeonites   _____ c. Forgery

4. Micah   _____ d. Bribery

5. Absalom   _____ e. Extortion

6. Samuel's Sons   _____ f. Fraud

7. Benjaminites   _____ g. Conspiracy

8. Jezebel   _____ h. Swindling

9. Rich Jews   _____ i. Arson

10. Ananias   _____ j. Murder

The Bible mentions the angel Gabriel only four times. He appeared twice before Daniel to teach him things he could not understand. He announced the birth of John the Baptist and told Mary of the conception of Jesus. Gabriel means God is mighty.

Cruel People

Answers on page 88

1. What cruel queen murdered all her grandchildren except one?

2. What mistress was cruel to her maid?

3. What king passed an edict, ordering the death of babies under age two?

4. Which of Jacob's sons did he describe as being cruel?

5. What Egyptian ruler cruelly mistreated Israelites?

6. What king had Zedekiah blinded and imprisoned for the remainder of his life?

7. What cruel woman demanded the head of John the Baptist?

8. What successor to a throne threatened to punish his subjects with scorpions?

9. Who hired assassins to slaughter 70 of his half brothers?

10. Who sacrificed his oldest son as a burnt offering on a wall?

Daughters

Answers on page 88

Match each daughter in the left-hand column, to her father, listed at the right.

1. Michal   ____ a. Jesse

2. Tamar   ____ b. Reuel

3. Rebekah   ____ c. David

4. Abigail   ____ d. Laban

5. Dinah   ____ e. Saul

6. Achsah   ____ f. Job

7. Leah   ____ g. Bethuel

8. Miriam   ____ h. Jacob

9. Zipporah   ____ i. Amram

10. Jemima   ____ j. Caleb

Q

Deceivers

Answers on page 88

1. Who pretended to be insane to deceive King Achish?

2. What servant tried to deceive his master and was stricken with leprosy as punishment?

3. What woman pretended to be a mourner to deceive David?

4. Who deceived his half-blind father by wearing goat skins on his hands?

5. What two men were deceitful, pretending their wives were their sisters?

6. Who deceived a king, telling him he had a secret message for him, and then killed him?

7. Who tried to deceive Peter by lying about a sale of property?

8. Who deceived a bridegroom on his wedding night?

9. What woman was given 1,100 pieces of silver to deceive a man into revealing the secret of his strength?

10. Who deceived relatives, pretending he did not know them, and accused them of being spies?

Q

Disciples

Answers on page 89

1. Who was the first disciple to whom Jesus said "Follow me"?

2. Who served as treasurer for the disciples?

3. Which disciple was a tax collector before joining Jesus' twelve?

4. What was Thomas' other name?

5. What was Thaddaeus' other name?

6. Which disciple was present at the miraculous feeding of the 5,000?

7. Which disciple tried to walk on water?

8. Which disciple did Jesus first see under a fig tree?

9. Who was the only disciple present at Jesus' crucifixion?

10. Which disciple was martyred by Herod?

Disguised People

Answers on page 89

1. Who disguised himself when he went to visit a witch?

2. What queen disguised herself when she went to visit a prophet?

3. To trick Joshua, who used a disguise of old clothing?

4. What son was disguised to fool his father?

5. What disguised king was fatally injured by archers during a battle?

6. What was the disguise of the prophet who waited by the roadside for the king of Israel?

7. What king went into battle disguised as an ordinary soldier?

8. What disguise did false prophets use that Jesus warned against?

9. Who "made himself strange" to his brothers so they would not recognize him?

10. What disguise did Joab have a woman use so she could meet with King David?

Dreamers

Answers on page 89

1. Who complained that God frightened him with dreams and nightmares?

2. Who dreamed of a tree that reached to heaven?

3. Who overheard a soldier's dream about hard bread overturning a tent?

4. Who had a dream of angels going up and down a ladder?

5. Who was so frightened by a character in his dream that his hair stood on end?

6. In a dream, God gave this man a choice of anything he wanted, and he chose wisdom.

7. What king dreamed of seven fat cows that came out of a river?

8. What man, because of a dream, arose in the middle of the night and set off on a trip with his wife and child?

9. Who dreamed that the sun, moon, and stars bowed to him?

10. What man was warned about his son-in-law in a dream?

Elderly People

Answers on page 89

Match each aged person listed at the left with his description at the right.

1. Caleb   ____ a. This bedridden, aged king was always cold no matter how many blankets were heaped upon him.

2. Asa   ____ b. This 147-year-old man made his son promise not to bury him in Egypt.

3. Methuselah   ____ c. This 85-year-old man asked to be given a mountain.

4. Barzillai   ____ d. This leader was still hale and hearty when he died at age 120 years.

5. Moses   ____ e. This king "in the time of his old age was diseased in his feet."

6. Solomon   ____ f. This 80-year-old man passed up an invitation to live in a king's house because of his advanced age.

7. Jacob   ____ g. This man lived longer than any other man in history.

8. David   ____ h. This king in his old age had his heart turned from God by his idolatrous wives.

Envious People

Answers on page 89

Match the people in the left-hand column to the person he or she envied, listed at the right.

1. Joshua   _____ a. Mordecai

2. Haman   _____ b. Leah

3. Princes and
   Presidents   _____ c. Jacob

4. Rachel   _____ d. Moses

5. Saul   _____ e. Eldad and
                               Medad

6. Laban's Sons   _____ f. Jesus

7. Miriam   _____ g. Daniel

8. Chief Priests   _____ h. Abel

9. Cain   _____ i. Isaac

10. Philistines   _____ j. David

The daily ration of meat for King Solomon's court was 20 cows, 100 sheep and 10 oxen as well as deer, gazelles and game birds (I Kings 4:23).

Q

Escapes

Answers on page 89

The people listed at the left made an escape.
Match them to their means of escape listed
at the right.

1. David

     ____ a. Drawn up from a dungeon by rotten rags.

2. Saul (Paul)

     ____ b. Let down from a window by a rope.

3. Noah

     ____ c. Found a dry path through a sea.

4. Ahimaaz and Jonathan

     ____ d. Let down a wall in a basket.

5. Apostles

     ____ e. A big fish spit him up.

6. Israelites

     ____ f. Used a horse for escape.

7. Jeremiah

     ____ g. His wife put an idol in his bed so he could escape.

8. Spies

     ____ h. Entered an ark.

9. Ben-Hadad

     ____ i. An angel opened prison gates.

10. Jonah

     ____ j. Hid in a well.

Q

The Faithful

Answers on page 90

Match the people in the left-hand column to the way they demonstrated their faith in God.

1. Joshua — a. Got ready for a flood, following God's instructions.

2. Moses — b. Made a dangerous journey to Jerusalem without military escort.

3. Nehemiah — c. Was willing to offer his son as a burnt offering.

4. Caleb and Joshua — d. Led the Israelites through the Red Sea to escape bondage.

5. Ezra — e. Knew he could rebuild a wall with God's help.

6. Abraham — f. Knew God would bring the Israelites into a land of milk and honey.

7. Noah — g. Knew by following God's orders he could take Jericho.

Q

Farmers

Answers on page 90

1. Who grew a tremendous crop that was 100 times the grain he sowed?

2. What king "loved husbandry"?

3. Who was the first "tiller of the soil"?

4. Who built booths for his cattle?

5. What farmer winnowed his barley at night?

6. Who plowed with 12 yoke of oxen?

7. Who threshed grain secretly in a wine press?

8. What king put 10 men in charge of his farm activities?

9. What farmers had their plowshares sharpened by Philistine smiths?

10. What prophet was a herdsman?

The rainbow was formed as a symbol to mankind that the world would never again be destroyed by a flood.

41

Q

Fasters

Answers on page 90

In the left-hand column are people who fasted.
Listed at the right are why, when, or where
they fasted. See if you can match them.

1. Moses   ____ a. Before having a dangerous interview with a king.

2. Ahab   ____ b. Because he had put a man in a lions' den.

3. Nehemiah   ____ c. As a way to worship God.

4. Jesus   ____ d. After being reproached by Elijah over his wickedness.

5. Esther   ____ e. Because of idolatrous marriages of returned exiles.

6. Darius   ____ f. While with God on a mountain.

7. Ezra   ____ g. While having visions.

8. Anna   ____ h. While being tempted by the devil.

9. Daniel   ____ i. After hearing about the run-down condition of Jerusalem.

Fathers

Answers on page 90

Match each father listed in the left-hand column, to his description at the right.

1. Job

____ a. He burned his son alive as a sacrifice to heathen gods.

2. Gideon

____ b. He became a father when he was 100 years old.

3. Abraham

____ c. He introduced his eight sons to a prophet.

4. Reuel

____ d. He had twin sons.

5. Isaac

____ e. He named a city after his son.

6. Jesse

____ f. He had four spinster daughters who were prophetesses.

7. Cain

____ g. He had the fairest daughters in the land.

8. Ahaz

____ h. He had seven daughters who were shepherdesses.

9. Philip

____ i. He had 70 sons.

*C*ontrary to popular belief, Delilah did not cut Samson's hair. She actually held his head in her lap as a Philistine soldier cut off his hair.

Q

Friends

Answers on page 90

1. Who befriended Paul when he was a prisoner?

2. Who were Job's three friends who sat with him for seven days and nights?

3. What two men experienced an immediate bond of friendship?

4. Who became a false friend to David?

5. What three people were warm, personal friends of Jesus?

6. What king and governor, who had been enemies, became friends during a trial?

7. What man and wife were friends of Paul?

8. What king was a friend and business associate of a father and son over a period of years?

9. Who was called "the friend of God"?

10. Who, when he got a promotion from a king, requested that his three friends be promoted also?

Frightened People

Answers on page 91

In the left-hand column are Bible people who experienced fear. At the right is the event that made them afraid. See if you can match them.

1. Israelites   ____ a. Angel with a sword

2. Joseph's brothers   ____ b. High waves

3. Saul   ____ c. Thunderstorm

4. Peter, James, John   ____ d. Man's shining face

5. Eliphaz   ____ e. Money in a sack

6. Belshazzar   ____ f. Voice coming out of a bright cloud

7. Peter   ____ g. Son-in-law

8. Nebuchadnezzar   ____ h. Handwriting on a wall

9. Aaron   ____ i. A spirit

10. David   ____ j. Dream

Q

Fugitives

Answers on page 91

1. What high priest became a fugitive because Saul was killing priests?

2. Who had to become a fugitive because he murdered his brother?

3. Who became a fugitive because of a jealous mistress?

4. Who became a fugitive because he stole his brother's blessing?

5. Who became a fugitive because he killed an Egyptian?

6. After a warning in a dream, who became a fugitive with his wife and child?

7. What king's son became a fugitive after having his half brother killed?

8. What fugitive, afraid of what King Achish might do to him, pretended to be insane?

9. Who became a fugitive to escape being killed by Solomon?

10. How were fugitives from Ephraim's army detected?

Q

Giants

Answers on page 91

These questions concern some of the "giants in the earth" (Gen. 6:4) of the Bible times.

1. What Philistine giant challenged Israelite armies and was killed by a lad armed with a slingshot?

2. What giant who tried to kill David was killed by Abishai?

3. What man, armed with only a staff, pulled a spear from a 7½-foot giant and used it to kill him?

4. What race of giants did Moses warn the Israelites they would encounter after crossing the river Jordan?

5. Who killed Lahmi, the brother of Goliath?

6. Who saw giants so large that it made them feel like grasshoppers in comparison?

7. What oversized king, the last survivor of a tribe of giants, had a huge bed?

8. Who killed a giant who had six fingers on each hand and six toes on each foot?

9. What tribe inherited the "valley of the giants"?

10. How many offspring of the "giant in Gath" were killed by David's troops?

Guests

Answers on page 91

Fill in each blank with the name of a guest
who fits the accompanying clue.

1. _____ was the guest of two sisters.

2. _____ was the guest of honor at a
dinner party given by
Samuel.

3. _____ was the guest for three
days of Publius, governor of
Melita.

4. _____ was provided with a guest
room prepared especially
for his visits.

5. _____ was given a serving
five times larger than
that served to the other
dinner guests.

6. _____ was accused of inhospitality
because he failed to kiss a
guest and anoint his head
with oil.

7. _____ was invited as a dinner
guest and ended up living
with his host and marrying
his daughter.

Q

Helpers

Answers on page 91

1. What woman helped the poor and needy?

2. What two men helped Moses win a battle by holding up his tired hands?

3. Who helped two spies make their escape?

4. What man and woman were Paul's "helpers in Christ"?

5. What military man told Abishai that if enemy Ammonites proved too strong for him to defeat, he would come and help him?

6. Who helped a man who had been attacked by bandits?

7. What fugitive helped some girls water their flocks?

8. Who said, "I delivered the poor that cried, and the fatherless, and him that had none to help him"?

9. Who helped Jesus carry the cross?

10. What prophetess agreed to help a military leader in an attack on the enemy?

Heroic People

Answers on page 92

The people listed at the left took a brave part in a Scripture event. See if you can match each person to the courageous act.

1. Jael _____ a. Conquered a city and won a wife for his reward.

2. Esther _____ b. Armed with only a tent pin, she killed an enemy captain.

3. Three Mighty Men _____ c. Attacked the armies of Midianites and Amalekites with only 300 men.

4. Shammah _____ d. Threw a millstone on the head of a military leader who was about to burn a city and killed him.

5. Woman of Thebes _____ e. Risked death in going before a king on behalf of the Jews.

6. Gideon _____ f. Broke through Philistine ranks to get a drink of water for a leader.

7. Othniel _____ g. When deserted by his soldiers, he stood alone in a field and beat back enemy Philistines.

Hospitable People

Answers on page 92

1. What girl was hospitable to a stranger, giving him a drink of water and watering his camels?

2. What priest with seven daughters welcomed a stranger who had appeared at a well?

3. What man on the island of Melita showed hospitality to shipwrecked strangers?

4. Who welcomed three strangers, inviting them to rest in the shade of a tree?

5. Who was told to go to Zarephath to receive a hospitable welcome from a widow?

6. Who said, "The stranger did not lodge in the street, but I opened my door to the traveler"?

7. Who welcomed two angels, inviting them to wash their feet and spend the night?

8. Who showed hospitality to a man because of a former friendship with the man's father?

9. What prominent woman showed hospitality to a prophet who stopped in at her home from time to time?

10. What man living in a rented house welcomed all who visited him?

Husbands

Answers on page 92

1. What husband had a wife who was turned into a pillar of salt?

2. What husband had a wife who said to him, "Dost thou still retain thine integrity? Curse God and die"?

3. What husband asked his wife, "Am I not better to thee than 10 sons?"

4. What husband had a wife who disapproved of his dancing in the street?

5. What husband was sent to war to be killed because another man coveted his wife?

6. What two husbands lied, saying their wives were their sisters?

7. What husband was exiled because of a disobedient wife?

8. What royal husband banished his wife because she disobeyed him?

9. What husband had 700 wives?

10. Who worked seven years to earn his wife?

Idolators

Answers on page 92

1. Who made molten images for Baal and burned incense under every green tree?

2. What sinful king set up two golden calves as idols?

3. Who placed a great golden image on a plain and commanded his subjects to fall down and worship it?

4. What king was drawn to idolatry by his wives?

5. What king rebuilt the heathen altars his father had broken down and encouraged his subjects to worship idols?

6. What king, after marrying a wicked queen, began the worship of Baal and built a temple and altar to Baal in Samaria?

7. What queen was removed from her throne because she had made an idol in a grove?

8. Who took earrings and made them into a golden calf for them to worship?

9. What king died a leper because he insisted on burning incense at the altar?

10. Who had an idol made from silver shekels her son had stolen from her, then returned?

Injured People

Answers on page 92

Fill in each blank with the name of an injured person who is described in the accompanying clue.

1. _____ was permanently crippled from childhood, after being dropped by his nurse.

2. _____ had his hip dislocated during a wrestling match with an angel.

3. _____ had his ear cut off by Peter.

4. _____ fell backward from a seat by a gate and broke his neck.

5. _____ had his eyes put out by the Babylonian enemy.

6. _____ fell from an upper window and was seriously injured.

7. _____ had his foot crushed against a wall by a mule.

8. _____ had his skull crushed by a piece of millstone thrown by a woman.

9. _____ shook his fist at a prophet, and his arm became paralyzed in that position.

In-Laws

Answers on page 93

1. Who gave good advice to his son-in-law?

2. Who was an unusually devoted daughter-in-law?

3. Who felt he was unworthy to become a king's son-in-law?

4. What father-in-law was given warning by God in a dream not to speak harshly to his son-in-law?

5. Whose mother-in-law was healed by Jesus?

6. What was the name of Naomi's daughter-in-law who did not take the trip back to Bethlehem?

7. Who had his wages changed 10 times by his father-in-law?

8. What former slave became the son-in-law of a powerful priest of On?

9. Who burned Philistine grain, and the Philistines then burned his father-in-law?

10. Who was invited by his brother-in-law to go on a long journey?

Jealous People

Answers on page 93

Some Scripture folk were miserably jealous. See if you can match these persons, listed in the left-hand column, with the persons they were jealous of.

1. Saul   _____ a. Mordecai

2. Philistines   _____ b. Moses

3. Rachel   _____ c. Jesus

4. Laban's Sons   _____ d. Isaac

5. Cain   _____ e. Hagar

6. Miriam   _____ f. David

7. Sarah   _____ g. Joseph

8. Chief Priests   _____ h. Jacob

9. Jacob's Sons   _____ i. Leah

10. Haman   _____ j. Abel

Before the great flood, people lived for an extremely long time. Methuselah, for example, lived 969 years. After that, the average life span was about 120 years.

Kind People

Answers on page 93

Fill in each blank with the name of a person(s)
who performed the kind act described in the
accompanying clue.

1. _____ showed kindness to a new
gleaner.

2. _____ provided for the poor by
not reaping field corners.

3. _____ cared for a wounded
traveler.

4. _____ fed shipwrecked men for
three days.

5. _____ was kind to an imprisoned
missionary.

6. _____ gave water to a traveler
and his camels.

7. _____ arranged for a lame man to
always eat at his table.

8. _____ made coats and garments
for the needy.

9. _____ brought supplies to a
fugitive.

10. _____ kept a room ready for a
prophet's use.

Kinfolk

Answers on page 93

In this gathering of Scripture kinfolk, see how many family ties you can identify.

WHAT RELATION IS:

1. Andrew to Peter _____

2. Othniel to Achsah _____

3. Mary to Elizabeth _____

4. Jethro to Moses _____

5. Hannah to Samuel _____

6. Lois to Timothy _____

7. Laban to Jacob _____

8. Bathsheba to Eliam _____

9. Lot to Abraham _____

10. Methuselah to Noah _____

The name Moses is based upon the Hebrew word *mashah*, which means "to draw out." He was so named because he was drawn out of the water.

Kings

Answers on page 93

Match the king to his description.

1. Asa   ____ a. Was cut in pieces by a prophet.

2. Saul   ____ b. Had a huge iron bed.

3. Hezekiah   ____ c. Ate grass like oxen.

4. Jehoiakim   ____ d. Had 4,000 stalls for his chariots and horses.

5. Solomon   ____ e. Tore a prophet's robe.

6. Nebuchadnezzar   ____ f. Was granted an extension on his life.

7. Agag   ____ g. Cut up a book and burned it.

8. David   ____ h. Saw handwriting on the wall.

9. Og   ____ i. Suffered with a foot disease.

10. Belshazzar   ____ j. Had a national census taken of his subjects.

Q

Leaders

Answers on page 94

1. After Moses' death, who became the new leader of the Israelites?

2. What imprisoned religious leader was released from jail by an angel?

3. What fugitive, while hiding in a cave, became the leader of hundreds of rebels?

4. Who refused to lead men into battle unless accompanied by a woman?

5. Who led a group of frightened men to Jerusalem?

6. What leader had problems with his followers?

7. After murdering a king, who blew a trumpet, mustered an army, and led them against enemy Moabites?

8. What leader obtained permission to escort a second colony of Jews to Jerusalem?

9. What military leader refused to be made king?

Q

Liars

Answers on page 94

1. Who lied about the sale of property?

2. What two men, at separate times, lied about their wives?

3. Who lied about the presence of spies?

4. What greedy servant lied to get money and clothing?

5. Who lied about his acquaintance with Jesus?

6. Who lied, denying a laugh of disbelief?

7. So that he might obtain provisions, who lied to a priest, pretending he had been sent from a king?

8. Who lied to cover up the murder of a brother?

9. Who told a series of three lies to a woman?

Q

Messengers

1. What man, pretending to be a messenger from God, murdered a king?

2. Who sent messengers to arrange a meeting with an estranged brother?

3. Who sent messengers to a king, asking permission for a company of people to pass through his country?

4. What king, injured by a fall, sent messengers to the god Baalzebub, asking if he would recover?

5. What prophet sent a messenger to a leprous man, telling him to wash seven times in the river Jordan?

6. Who sent messengers to a man's tent to look for stolen property?

7. Who said a messenger of Satan was sent to "buffet" him?

8. What king sent out messengers to find a harpist?

9. What prophet offered to be a messenger for God, saying, "Here am I; send me"?

10. Who sent out messengers with letters decreeing that all Jews were to be destroyed?

Miracle Workers

Answers on page 94

Listed at the left are 10 miracle workers. In the right-hand column their outstanding deeds are described. See if you can match them.

1. Moses —— a. Healed a lame man.

2. Jesus —— b. Made a sundial's shadow go backward 10 degrees.

3. Aaron —— c. Made an iron axehead float on water.

4. Samson —— d. Turned water into wine.

5. Peter —— e. Made the sun and moon stand still.

6. Elisha —— f. Got water from a rock.

7. Isaiah —— g. Killed 1,000 men with the jawbone of an ass.

8. Paul —— h. Changed a rod into a serpent.

9. Joshua —— i. Restored life to a man who had fallen from a high window.

Q

Mothers

Answers on page 94

1. Who was the "mother of all living"?

2. What mother "lent her child to the Lord"?

3. What mother urged her daughter to ask for a man's head?

4. What mother asked Jesus if her two sons could sit on His right and left hand in His kingdom?

5. What mother helped her son deceive his father?

6. What mother served as a paid nurse for her baby son?

7. What 90-year-old woman became a mother?

8. What mother arranged for her son to marry an Egyptian girl?

In biblical times, being without a child was a great misfortune. Sarah, at age 90, was the oldest woman in the Bible to bear a child. She is also the woman most often mentioned (56 times).

Q

Murderers

Answers on page 94

1. Who was the first murderer mentioned in the Bible?

2. What left-handed man murdered a fat king?

3. What grandmother murdered all her grandchildren, except one little boy?

4. What two men murdered a man as he took a noontime nap?

5. Who murdered a man who refused to stop chasing him?

6. What woman gave a man a drink of milk and then murdered him?

7. Who put a wet blanket on a king's face, smothering him to death?

8. Who became a fugitive because he murdered a cruel Egyptian?

9. Who murdered a half-drunk king and then killed the entire royal family?

10. Who attempted murder with a javelin?

Musicians

Answers on page 95

1. Who made a sound with cymbals?

2. What prophetess played the timbrel?

3. What king organized Levites at the temple into an orchestral group?

4. Who invented the harp and organ?

5. Who was a skillful harp player?

6. Who said, "I am become as sounding brass, or a tinkling cymbal"?

7. Who hung their harps "upon the willows"?

8. How many Levites did David appoint to furnish instrumental music for temple worship?

9. At the anointing of which king did the people "pipe with pipes"?

10. On what occasion did David and "all the house of Israel play before the Lord on all manner of instruments...even on harps, and on psalteries, and on timbrels, and on cornets and on cymbals"?

Obedient People

Answers on page 95

The people listed at the left were rewarded in various ways for their obedience to God. Their rewards are listed at the right. See if you can match them.

1. Elijah   _____ a. Buried among kings

2. Abram   _____ b. Deliverance from enemies

3. Caleb   _____ c. Fed by ravens

4. Noah   _____ d. Could build fortified cities, for his land was at peace

5. Joshua   _____ e. Riches and honor

6. Hezekiah   _____ f. Conquered an entire land

7. Jehoshaphat   _____ g. Saved from a watery disaster

8. Jehoiada   _____ h. Descendants multiplied like stars in the sky

9. David   _____ i. Prospered in everything he did

10. Asa   _____ j. Possession of land

Poor People

Answers on page 95

Match each poor person in the left-hand column to the unprosperous circumstance listed at the right.

1. David

2. Lazarus

3. Gideon

4. Prodigal Son

5. Israelites

6. Macedonians

7. Widow of Zarephath

____ a. Even though poverty-stricken, gave money to a cause.

____ b. Told God his family was the poorest in the tribe of Manasseh.

____ c. "When he had spent all, there arose a mighty famine in the land; and he began to be in want."

____ d Lay at a rich man's gate hoping to be fed with crumbs.

____ e. He felt he was unworthy to be a king's son-in-law because he was poor.

____ f. Had only a small amount of food to eat.

____ g. Had to mortgage property, borrow money, and lose children to bondage.

Praying People

Answers on page 95

Fill in each blank with the name of the person who made the accompanying petition.

1. _____ prayed for a drought.

2. _____ prayed for victory over an enemy.

3. _____ prayed for a drink of water.

4. _____ prayed for a blessing on his house.

5. _____ prayed for a son.

6. _____ prayed for the healing of a leprosy case.

7. _____ prayed for protection from a brother.

8. _____ prayed to be returned to Jerusalem and his kingdom.

9. _____ prayed for the blinding of an army.

10. _____ prayed for guidance in bringing up a child.

Preachers

Answers on page 95

1. Who preached so long that one of his listeners fell asleep and tumbled from a high window to his death?

2. Which book of the Bible includes the word "Preacher" in its subtitle?

3. Whose preaching caused the king of Nineveh to step down from his throne, put on sackcloth, and sit in ashes?

4. What prophet said, "The Lord hath anointed me to preach good tidings"?

5. Who received instructions to preach "upon the housetops"?

6. Who preached in the wilderness of Judaea?

7. Who so angered people with his preaching that they tried to push him over a cliff?

8. Whose preaching on the day of Pentecost resulted in about 3,000 people being converted and baptized?

9. What early Bible person did Peter call a "preacher of righteousness"?

10. Whose preaching brought about the conversion of Simon the sorcerer?

Priests

Answers on page 96

Fill in each blank with the name of a priest who fits the accompanying description.

1. _____ was Joseph's father-in-law.

2. _____ bored a hole in the lid of a chest and used it to hold money contributions.

3. _____ succeeded Aaron as high priest.

4. _____ returned to Jerusalem with his countrymen.

5. _____ had wicked sons.

6. _____ gave David shewbread and Goliath's sword.

7. _____ was the only priest to escape Doeg's slaughter of priests.

8. _____ was instructed to make an altar, copying one seen by Ahaz.

9. _____ became the first high priest of Israel.

10. _____ was involved in a plot to destroy Jesus.

Q

Answers on page 96

Prophets

Fill in each blank with the name of the prophet who fits the accompanying description.

1. _____ was suspended between heaven and earth by a lock of his hair.

2. _____ saw horses of different colors on mountains of brass.

3. _____ wrote the shortest book in the Old Testament.

4. _____ was mocked by children because of his bald head.

5. _____ cultivated sycamore trees.

6. _____ was put in stocks.

7. _____ had a remedy for boils.

8. _____ spent three days and nights inside a fish.

9. _____ was swept up to heaven by a whirlwind.

10. _____ spent a night in a lions' den.

Q

Scribes

Answers on page 96

1. David's uncle was a "counselor, a wise man, and a scribe." What was his name?

2. What scribe was sent by King Hezekiah with a message to Isaiah?

3. Who denounced scribes?

4. What scribe wrote to King Artaxerxes, opposing the rebuilding of Jerusalem?

5. To what scribe did Hilkiah give a scroll to read?

6. What scribe did Nehemiah appoint as treasurer of Jerusalem's storehouses?

7. What scribe kept the muster roll of Uzziah's host of fighting men?

8. To what scribe did Jeremiah dictate his prophecy?

9. What scribe read the book of Moses' law from a wooden pulpit?

10. Who called in a king's scribes and dictated letters to them to be sent throughout the kingdom?

 *T*he story of how Jonah disobeyed God, yet was saved from drowning by being swallowed by a whale, is popular around the world. But the Bible never mentions a whale – only a "great fish" and a "large sea monster." (Book of Jonah, chapters 1-2)

Q

Singers

Answers on page 96

1. What two prisoners sang hymns in prison at midnight?

2. Who sang in front of a golden calf?

3. What king wrote 1,005 songs?

4. Where did the disciples go after they had sung a hymn?

5. What king who was slain in battle was mourned in song by temple choirs?

6. What two people sang a victory song?

7. What king had a singing choir lead the march into battle?

8. Who sang a song that mentioned God having a horse and rider thrown into the sea?

9. How were singers chosen for their term of service in the tabernacle?

Unicorns are mentioned in the Bible nine times. The animal is actually an oryx – a white antelope-like creature with two long, straight horns. Almost faced with extinction in the 19th century, they are now making a comeback with the help of naturalists.

Soldiers

Answers on page 96

1. What Roman soldier was converted by Peter?

2. What woman helped command 10,000 soldiers?

3. Which of David's soldiers saved him from being killed by a giant?

4. What drink did soldiers offer Jesus while He was on the cross?

5. Paul was in the custody of what soldier when they encountered a storm at sea?

6. On David's orders, what soldier was sent to the front lines so he would be killed?

7. What brother, serving as a soldier, scolded a younger brother for coming to the battlefield?

8. According to the Israelite law, how long was a newly-married man exempt from being drafted into the army?

9. What king's son and his armor-bearer showed great bravery in attacking an enemy garrison?

10. What soldier was with David at Pasdammim and killed Philistines in a barley field?

Sons

Answers on page 97

Match the sons listed in the left column to their descriptions listed on the right.

1. Jonathan

_____ a. Fell into his father's arms and wept a long time.

2. Esau

_____ b. Was the adopted son of a princess.

3. Timothy

_____ c. Became so angry with his father he left the table without eating.

4. Absalom

_____ d. Said, "I...am no more worthy to be called thy son: make me as one of thy hired servants."

5. Jacob

_____ e. Kept his father supplied with venison.

6. Asa

_____ f. Conspired against his father.

7. Moses

_____ g. Was like a son to Paul.

8. Joseph

_____ h. Removed his mother from being queen because she made an idol.

9. Prodigal Son

_____ i. Deceived his father to get his blessing.

Thieves

Answers on page 97

1. Who confessed to his mother that he had stolen pieces of silver from her?

2. What thief was released instead of Jesus?

3. Who stole household idols from her father?

4. Who stole and hid a wedge of gold, silver, and a Babylonian robe?

5. How many spies robbed Micah of images, ephod and teraphim?

6. What king of Egypt ransacked the temple and stole the gold shield that Solomon had made?

7. Men of what district set up ambushes on a mountaintop and robbed passers-by?

8. Which of the disciples was in charge of the disciples' funds and often dipped into them for his own use?

9. Who said, "I robbed other churches, taking wages of them, to do you service"?

10. Who was falsely accused of having stolen a silver cup?

Travelers

Answers on page 97

1. Who insisted on traveling with a prophet, going with him from Bethel to Jericho?

2. Who traveled with a mother-in-law to Bethlehem?

3. Who was a fellow traveler of Saul (Paul) when he set out on his first missionary tour?

4. Who walked alongside two disciples, traveling together to Emmaus?

5. Who traveled to Egypt accompanied by 70 descendants?

6. Who, because of a dream, traveled in the middle of the night with his wife and child?

7. Which uncle and nephew were fellow travelers?

8. What men who were traveling in a group were not allowed to carry food, money or extra clothing?

9. Who traveled with a servant, enroute to a marriage?

10. How many brothers traveled together to buy grain?

Wealthy People

Answers on page 97

Match the names of these wealthy people of Scripture times with their descriptions.

1. Zacchaeus   ____ a. He became so wealthy he had to construct special treasury buildings to hold his riches.

2. Jehoshaphat   ____ b. He "exceeded all the kings of the earth for riches."

2. Nabal   ____ c. He was told to dispose of his wealth and give to the poor.

4. Rich young ruler   ____ d. His wealth came from tax collecting.

5. Ahasuerus   ____ e. He was the first man mentioned in the Bible as being very rich.

6. Hezekiah   ____ f. He held a six-month celebration to display his wealth.

7. Abram   ____ g. His willing subjects paid him so many taxes he became very wealthy.

8. Solomon   ____ h. Although wealthy, he was stingy and rude.

Wives

Answers on page 97

Match each wife to her description.

1. Vashti   —— a. She was given to her husband as a reward for conquering a city.

2. Jezebel   —— b. Traveled a long way by camel to marry a man she had never seen.

3. Rebekah   —— c. Refused to display her beauty to her husband's banquet guests.

4. Abigail   —— d. Was the first wife to get her husband in trouble.

5. Zeresh   —— e. Joined her husband in a lie about selling property.

6. Eve   —— f. Told her husband to make a gallows.

7. Sapphira   —— g. Disobeyed her husband and supplied a man and his soldiers with provisions.

8. Achsah   —— h. Arranged to get her husband a vineyard.

Answers

ACCUSERS

1. Joseph (Gen. 42:8, 9)
2. Saul (I Sam. 22:7, 8)
3. Asian Jews (Acts 21:27, 28)
4. They were thrown into a lion's den (Dan. 6:1-24)
5. Unjust steward (Luke 16:1, 2)
6. Demetrius (Acts 19:24-27)
7. Irijah (Jer. 37:12-14)
8. Korah (Num. 16:1-5)
9. Pharisees (Matt. 12:1, 2)
10. Jezebel (I Kings 21:6-10)

ANGRY PEOPLE

1. Moses (Exod. 11:8)
2. Eliab (I Sam. 17:28)
3. Saul (I Sam. 11:4-7)
4. Nebuchadnessar (Dan. 3:19, 20)
5. Cain (Gen. 4:4-6)
6. Balaam (Num. 22:27)
7. Ahasuerus (Esther 7:7)
8. Jonathan (I Sam. 20:34)

AUTHORS

1. Moses (Exod. 17:14)
2. John (Rev. 1:10, 11)
3. Jesus (Luke 4:16, 17)
4. David (Ps. 45:1)
5. Jeremiah (Jer. 51:60-63)
6. Job (Job 19:23)
7. Solomon (I Kings 4:32)

8. Samuel (I Sam. 10:25)
9. Obadiah
10. Nathan (II Chron. 9:29)

BABIES

1. Moses (Exod. 2:10)
2. Isaac (Gen. 21:8)
3. Moses (Exod. 2:7-9)
4. Obed (Ruth 4:15-17)
5. Jacob (Gen. 25:24-26)
6. Benjamin (Gen. 35:18)
7. Job (Job 3:11)
8. Cain (Gen. 4:1)
9. Jesus (Luke 2:8-12)
10. John (Luke 1:13, 60)

BEAUTIFUL PEOPLE

1. Ahasuerus (Esther 1:3, 10, 11)
2. Absolom (II Sam. 14:25)
3. David (I Sam. 16:11, 12)
4. Job (Job 42:15)
5. Esther (Esther 2:2-17)
6. Rebekah (Gen. 24:16-18)
7. Saul (I Sam. 9:2)
8. Bathsheba (II Sam. 11:1-3)
9. Joseph (Gen. 39:1, 6)
10. Rachel (Gen. 29:17, 18)

BEREAVED PEOPLE

1. Aaron (Lev. 10:1, 2, 6)
2. Naomi (Ruth 1:1-5, 20)
3. Ezekiel (Ezek. 24:15-18)
4. Joseph (Gen. 50:4-6)

Answers

5. Abraham (Gen. 23:1-6)
6. Job (Job 1:1, 2, 18-20)
7. David (II Sam. 18:33)
8. Jairus (Luke 8:41-50)
9. Jacob (Gen. 35:19, 20)

BLESSERS

A. 7 (Luke 2:33, 34)
B. 8 (I Sam. 2:20)
C. 6 (Deut. 33:1)
D. 2 (Josh. 14:13)
E. 10 (Judg. 5:1, 24)
F. 9 (Gen. 47:7)
G. 1 (Gen. 27:27, 30)
H. 3 (Gen. 31:55)
I. 5 (II Sam. 19:39)
J. 4 (Gen. 14:18, 19)

BLIND PEOPLE

1. (a) Nahash (I Sam. 11:1, 2)
2. (c) Ahijah (I Kings 14:2-4)
3. (c) Elisha (II Kings 6:18)
4. (a) Elymas (Acts 13:8-11)
5. (b) Lot (Gen. 19:1-11)
6. (c) Isaac (Gen. 27)
7. (a) Zedekiah
   (II Kings 25:5-7)
8. (c) Bartimaeus
   (Mark 10:46-52)

BOYS

1. Mephibosheth (II Sam. 4:4)
2. Enoch (Gen. 4:17)
3. Isaac (Gen. 22:6-8)

4. Jesus (Luke 2:42-47)
5. Joseph (Gen. 37:2, 3)
6. Ephraim and Manasseh
   (Gen. 48:1-10)
7. Samuel (I Sam. 2:18, 19)
8. Joash (II Chron. 24:1)
9. Shunammite's Son
   (II Kings 4:1, 18-35)
10. Ishmael (Gen. 21:9-19)

BROTHERS

A. 5 (Matt. 4:18)
B. 6 (Gen. 27:41)
C. 8 (Matt. 4:21, 22)
D. 2 (Lev. 10:1, 2)
E. 7 (I Sam. 17:28)
F. 1 (I Kings 2:22-25)
G. 9 (Judg. 1:3)
H. 4 (Exod. 4:14-15)
I. 3 (Gen. 4:25)

BUILDERS

1. Omri (Kings 16:23, 24)
2. Jacob (Gen. 33:17)
3. Uzziah (II Chron. 26:9)
4. Paul (I Cor. 3:10)
5. Bezaleel (Exod. 35:30-35;
   37:1; 38:1-7)
6. Jotham (II Chron. 27:1, 4)
7. Noah (Gen. 6:14-16)
8. Hezekiah (II Chron. 32:30)

BUSINESS PEOPLE

1. Joseph (Gen. 41:54-57)
2. Paul (Acts 18:1-3)

Answers

3. Elisha (II Kings 4:2-7)
4. Lydia (Acts 16:14)
5. Jehoshaphat and Ahaziah
   (II Chron. 20:35, 36)
6. Demetrius (Acts 19:24-27)
7. Ezekiel (Ezek. 27)
8. Levi (Luke 5:27, 28)
9. Hiram (I Chron. 14:1;
   II Chron. 2:11, 16)
10. Solomon (I Kings 10:28)

BUYERS

A. 2 (Gen. 23:13-19)
B. 4 (Gen. 47:20)
C. 6 (Ruth 4:10)
D. 7 (Mark 15:43, 46)
E. 1 (Gen. 39:1)
F. 8 (Gen. 33:18, 19)
G. 3 (II Sam. 24:24)
H. 9 (I Kings 16:23, 24)
I. 10 (Mark 16:1)
J. 5 (Matt. 27:6, 7)

CAPTAINS

1. Naaman (II Kings 5:1)
2. Adino (II Sam. 23:8)
3. Sisera (Judg. 4:2, 18, 21)
4. Abner (I Sam. 14:50)
5. Claudius Lysias
   (Acts 23:18, 26, 27)
6. Potiphar (Gen. 37:36)
7. Jephthah (Judg. 11:1,
   5, 6)
8. David (I Sam. 22:1, 2)

9. Amasa (II Sam. 19:13)
10. Nebuzar-adan
    (II Kings 25:8, 9)

CAPTIVES

1. Lot (Gen. 14:9-16)
2. Jehoiachin
   (II Kings 25:27-30)
3. Ezekiel (Ezek. 1:1)
4. Joseph (Gen. 41:1-41)
5. Daniel (Dan. 1:3-6)
6. Zedekiah (Jer. 52:9-11)
7. Jews (Ps. 137:2, 3)
8. Jehoiachin
   (II Kings 24:11-16)
9. Ezra
10. Mordecai (Esther 2:5; 8:1,
    2, 15)

CATTLEMEN

1. Elisha (I Kings 19:19)
2. Obadiah and Ahab
   (I Kings 18:5, 6)
3. Job (Job 1:3, 14, 15)
4. Jacob (Gen. 33:17)
5. Abraham and Lot
   (Gen. 13:1-9)
6. Amos (Amos 1:1)
7. Isaac (Gen. 26:12-15)
8. Laban (Gen. 30:27-30)
9. Doeg the Edomite
   (I Sam. 21:7)
10. Jabal (Gen. 4:20)

Answers

CONCEALERS

A. 8 (Josh. 7:20, 21)
B. 9 (Gen. 31:19, 34)
C. 1 (Exod. 2:1-3; 6:20)
D. 10 (II Kings 11:2, 3)
E. 7 (Matt. 25:14-18)
F. 5 (Exod. 2:11, 12)
G. 4 (Gen. 35:2-4)
H. 2 (I Kings 18:4)
I. 6 (Josh. 2:3-6)
J. 3 (Jer. 43:9)

CONSPIRATORS

A. 10 (I Kings 16:8-10)
B. 7 (Gen. 37:17, 18)
C. 1 (II Sam. 15:1-12)
D. 9 (Matt. 22:15-18)
E. 2 (II Kings 12:20)
F. 4 (Judg. 9:23-41)
G. 3 (Judg. 16:4-21)
H. 6 (II Kings 9:14-24)
I. 5 (Acts 23:12-21)
J. 8 (I Sam. 22:7-13)

CONVERTS

1. Saul (Paul) (Acts 9:1-20)
2. About 3,000 (Acts 2:41)
3. Cornelius (Acts 10)
4. Philip (Acts 8:26-38)
5. Saul (I Sam. 10:5-7)
6. Simon (Acts 8:9-13)
7. Nebuchadnezzar (Dan. 4)
8. Lydia (Acts 16:14, 15)
9. Simon Peter (Luke 22:31, 32)
10. Sergius Paulus (Acts 13:7-12)

COURAGEOUS PEOPLE

A. 5 (Dan. 6:6-10)
B. 6 (Mark 15:43)
C. 8 (II Sam. 23:11, 12)
D. 2 (Num. 16:46-48)
E. 7 (Neh. 6:10-13)
F. 1 (Judg. 7:15-21)
G. 3 (I Sam. 17:4, 40)
H. 4 (II Sam. 23:20, 21)

COVENANTERS

A. 9 (Gen. 9:12-16)
B. 3 (I Kings 15:18, 19)
C. 8 (I Sam. 11:1, 2)
D. 2 (I Sam. 1:11)
E. 1 (I Kings 5:8-11)
F. 7 (I Sam. 18:3, 4)
G. 5 (Gen. 21:30)
H. 10 (Gen. 31:46-52)
I. 6 (Matt. 26:14, 15)
J. 4 (Josh. 2:2-20)

COVETOUS PEOPLE

1. Achan (Josh. 7:20, 21)
2. Ahab (I Kings 21:1, 2)
3. Paul (Acts 20:33)
4. Gehazi (II Kings 5:15-24)
5. Balaam (II Peter 2:15)

Answers

6. Simon Magus (Acts 8:9, 17-19)
7. Pharisees (Luke 16:14, 15)
8. Felix (Acts 24:25, 26)
9. Eve (Gen. 3:6)
10. Ananias (Acts 5:1, 2)

COWARDS

A. 4 (Exod. 32:1-5, 22-24)
B. 5 (Matt. 8:26)
C. 7 (Luke 22:54-60)
D. 8 (Judg. 6:25-27)
E. 3 (I Sam. 17:21-24)
F. 1 (John 19:12-16)
G. 2 (Gen. 3:11, 12)
H. 6 (Gen. 12:11-13)

CRIMINALS

A. 7 (Judg. 21:20-23)
B. 4 (Judg. 17:1, 2)
C. 8 (I Kings 21:8)
D. 6 (I Sam. 8:1-3)
E. 9 (Neh. 5:1-13)
F. 3 (Josh. 9:3-15)
G. 5 (II Sam. 15:1-6)
H. 10 (Acts 5:1-3)
I. 2 (Judg. 15:4, 5)
J. 1 (Judg. 3:16-22)

CRUEL PEOPLE

1. Athaliah (II Kings 11:1-3)
2. Sarah (Gen. 16:6)
3. Herod (Matt. 2:16)
4. Simeon and Levi
   (Gen. 49:5-7)

5. Pharaoh (Exod. 5:6-18)
6. Nebuchadnezzar
   (Jer. 52:4, 10, 11)
7. Herodias (Matt. 14:3-10)
8. Rehoboam (I Kings 12:11, 12)
9. Abimelech (Judg. 9:1-5)
10. King of Moab
    (II Kings 3:26, 27)

DAUGHTERS

A. 4 (I Chron. 2:13, 16)
B. 9 (Exod. 2:18, 21)
C. 2 (I Chron. 3:9)
D. 7 (Gen. 29:16)
E. 1 (I Sam. 18:20)
F. 10 (Job 42:14)
G. 3 (Gen. 24:15)
H. 5 (Gen. 30:19, 21)
I. 8 (I Chron. 6:3)
J. 6 (Judg. 1:12)

DECEIVERS

1. David (I Sam. 21:10-15)
2. Gehazi (II Kings 5:20-27)
3. Woman of Tekoa
   (II Sam. 14:1-19)
4. Jacob (Gen. 27:1-23)
5. Abraham and Isaac
   (Gen. 12:12, 13; 26:7-10)
6. Ehud (Judg. 3:15-23)
7. Ananias (Acts 5:1-4)
8. Laban (Gen. 29:18-25)
9. Delilah (Judg. 16:5-19)
10. Joseph (Gen. 42:7-17)

Answers

DISCIPLES

1. Philip (John 1-43)
2. Judas (John 12:4-6; 13:29)
3. Matthew (Matt. 9:9)
4. Didymus (John 21:2)
5. Lebbaeus (Matt. 10:3)
6. Andrew (John 6:8, 9)
7. Peter (Matt. 14:28-31)
8. Nathanael (John 1:47, 48)
9. John (John 19:25-27)
10. James (Acts 12:1, 2)

DISGUISED PEOPLE

1. Saul (I Sam. 28:8)
2. Jeroboam's wife (I Kings 14:2)
3. Gibeonites (Josh. 9:3-6)
4. Jacob (Gen. 27:15-23)
5. Josiah (II Chron. 35:22-24)
6. Ashes on his face (I Kings 20:38)
7. Ahab (II Chron. 18:3, 29)
8. Sheeps' clothing (Matt. 7:15)
9. Joseph (Gen. 42:7)
10. Mourner (II Sam. 14:1-4)

DREAMERS

1. Job (Job 7:14)
2. Nebuchadnezzar (Dan. 4:4-11)
3. Gideon (Judg. 7:13)
4. Jacob (Gen. 28:10-12)
5. Eliphaz (Job 4:13-15)
6. Solomon (I Kings 3:5-9)
7. Pharaoh (Gen. 41:17, 18)
8. Joseph (Matt. 2:13, 14)
9. Joseph (Gen. 37:5, 9)
10. Laban (Gen. 31:24)

ELDERLY PEOPLE

A. 8 (I Kings 1:1)
B. 7 (Gen. 47:28-31)
C. 1 (Josh. 14:7-12)
D. 5 (Deut. 34:7)
E. 2 (I Kings 15:23)
F. 4 (II Sam. 19:33-35)
G. 3 (Gen. 5:27)
H. 6 (I Kings 11:3, 4)

ENVIOUS PEOPLE

A. 2 (Esther 5:11-13)
B. 4 (Gen. 30:1)
C. 6 (Gen. 31:1)
D. 7 (Num. 12:1, 2)
E. 1 (Num. 11:27-29)
F. 8 (Mark 15:1, 10)
G. 3 (Dan. 6:3, 4)
H. 9 (Gen. 4:4, 5)
I. 10 (Gen. 26:12-14)
J. 5 (I Sam. 18:6-8)

ESCAPES

A. 7 (Jer. 38:7-13)
B. 8 (Josh. 2:1-15)
C. 6 (Exod. 14:29, 30)
D. 2 (Acts 9:23-25)

Answers

E. 10 (Jonah 2:10)
F. 9 (I Kings 20:20)
G. 1 (I Sam. 19:12-18)
H. 3 (Gen. 7)
I. 5 (Acts 5:18, 19)
J. 4 (II Sam. 17:17-19)

THE FAITHFUL

A. 7 (Gen. 6:14-22)
B. 5 (Ezra 8:22, 31)
C. 6 (Gen. 22:1-12)
D. 2 (Exod. 14:13-22)
E. 3 (Neh. 2:17-20)
F. 4 (Num. 14:6-9)
G. 1 (Josh. 6:1-16)

FARMERS

1. Isaac (Gen. 26:12)
2. Uzziah (II Chron. 26:9, 10)
3. Cain (Gen. 4:2)
4. Jacob (Gen. 33:17)
5. Boaz (Ruth 3:2)
6. Elisha (I Kings 19:19)
7. Gideon (Judg. 6:11)
8. David (I Chron. 27:26-31)
9. Israelites (I Sam. 13:20, 21)
10. Amos (Amos 1:1)

FASTERS

A. 5 (Esther 4:15, 16)
B. 6 (Dan. 6:16-18)
C. 8 (Luke 2:36, 37)
D. 2 (I Kings 21:20-27)

E. 7 (Ezra 10:2, 6)
F. 1 (Exod. 34:4, 28)
G. 9 (Dan. 10:1-3)
H. 4 (Matt. 4:1, 2)
I. 3 (Neh. 1:1-4)

FATHERS

A. 8 (II Kings 16:2-3)
B. 3 (Gen. 21:5)
C. 6 (I Sam. 16:8-12)
D. 5 (Gen. 25:21-24)
E. 7 (Gen. 4:17)
F. 9 (Acts 21:8, 9)
G. 1 (Job 42:15)
H. 4 (Exod. 2:16, 18)
I. 2 (Judg. 8:30)

FRIENDS

1. Onesiphorus (II Tim. 1:16, 17)
2. Eliphaz, Bildad, Zophar (Job 2:11, 13)
3. David and Jonathan (I Sam. 18:1-3)
4. Hushai (II Sam. 16:16-18)
5. Mary, Martha, Lazarus (John 11:5)
6. Herod and Pilate (Luke 23:6-12)
7. Aquila and Priscilla (Rom. 16:3, 4)
8. Hiram (I Kings 5:1; II Sam. 5:11)
9. Abraham (James 2:23)
10. Daniel (Dan. 2:48, 49)

Answers

FRIGHTENED PEOPLE

A. 10 (I Chron. 21:16, 30)
B. 7 (Matt. 14:29, 30)
C. 1 (I Sam. 12:1, 17, 18)
D. 9 (Exod. 34:29, 30)
E. 2 (Gen. 42:27, 28)
F. 4 (Matt. 17:1, 5-7)
G. 3 (I Sam. 18:28, 29)
H. 6 (Dan. 5:1-6)
I. 5 (Job 4:13-15)
J. 8 (Dan. 4:4, 5)

FUGITIVES

1. Abiathar
   (I Sam. 22:17-23)
2. Cain (Gen. 4:8-12)
3. Hagar (Gen. 21:9-14)
4. Jacob (Gen. 27:41-43)
5. Moses (Exod. 2:11-15)
6. Joseph (Matt. 2:13, 14)
7. Absalom (II Sam. 13:28, 38)
8. David (I Sam. 21:10-13)
9. Jeroboam (I Kings 11:40)
10. By the way they pronounced the words 'shibboleth' (Judg. 12:5, 6)

GIANTS

1. Goliath (I Sam. 17:4-10; 48-50)
2. Ishbi-benob (II Sam. 21:15-17)
3. Benaiah (I Chron. 11:22, 23)
4. Anaks (Deut. 9:1, 2)
5. Elhanan (I Chron. 20:5)
6. Moses' spies (Num. 13:17, 33)
7. Og (Deut. 3:11)
8. Jonathan, David's nephew (II Sam. 21:20, 21)
9. Benjamin (Josh. 18:11-16)
10. Four (II Sam. 21:16-22)

GUESTS

1. Jesus (Luke 10:38-40)
2. Saul (I Sam. 9:19-24)
3. Paul (Acts 28:1, 7)
4. Elisha (II Kings 4:8-10)
5. Benjamin (Gen. 43:31-34)
6. Simon (Luke 7:40-46)
7. Moses (Exod. 2:15-21)

HELPERS

1. Dorcas (Acts 9:36)
2. Aaron and Hur (Exod. 17:11, 12)
3. Rahab (Josh. 2:1-16)
4. Aquila and Priscilla (Rom. 16:3)
5. Joab (I Chron. 19:8-12)
6. Good Samaritan (Luke 10:30-35)
7. Moses (Exod. 2:15-17)
8. Job (Job 29:12)

Answers

9. Simon of Cyrene
(Matt. 27:32)
10. Deborah (Judg. 4:4-10)

HEROIC PEOPLE

A. 7 (Judg. 1:12, 13)
B. 1 (Judg. 4:17-21)
C. 6 (Judg. 7:7-23)
D. 5 (Judg. 9:50-55)
E. 2 (Esther 4:8-16)
F. 3 (II Sam. 23:13-16)
G. 4 (II Sam. 23:11, 12)

HOSPITABLE PEOPLE

1. Rebekah (Gen. 24:45, 46)
2. Reuel (Exod. 2:16-20)
3. Publius (Acts 27:44; 28:7)
4. Abram (Gen. 18:1-4)
5. Elijah (I Kings 17:8, 9)
6. Job (Job 31:32)
7. Lot (Gen. 19:1, 2)
8. David to Mephibosheth
(II Sam. 9:7-13)
9. Shunammite woman
(II Kings 4:8-10)
10. Paul (Acts 28:30)

HUSBANDS

1. Lot (Gen. 19:15, 26)
2. Job (Job 2:9)
3. Elkanah (I Sam. 1:8)
4. David (II Sam. 6:14, 16)
5. Uriah (II Sam. 11:6-17,

26, 27)
6. Abraham and Isaac
(Gen. 12:11-19; 26:7-10)
7. Adam (Gen. 3)
8. Ahasuerus
(Esther 1:10-19)
9. Solomon (I Kings 11:3)
10. Jacob (Gen. 29:18, 20)

IDOLATORS

1. Ahaz (II Chron. 28:1-4)
2. Jeroboam
(I Kings 12:26-30)
3. Nebuchadnezzar
(Dan. 3:1-5)
4. Solomon (I Kings 11:4)
5. Manasseh
(II Chron. 33:1-3)
6. Ahab (I Kings 16:30-33)
7. Maachah (II Chron. 15:16)
8. Aaron (Exod. 32:2-6)
9. Uzziah
(II Chron. 26:16-21)
10. Micah's mother
(Judg. 17:1-4)

INJURED PEOPLE

1. Mephibosheth
(II Sam. 4:4)
2. Jacob (Gen. 32:24, 25)
3. Malchus (John 18:10)
4. Eli (I Sam. 4:16-18)
5. Zedekiah (II Kings 25:5-7)
6. Ahaziah (II Kings 1:2)

Answers

7. Balaam (Num. 22:25)
8. Abimelech (II Sam. 11:21)
9. Jeroboam (I Kings 13:1-4)

IN-LAWS

1. Jethro (Exod. 18:6, 14-24)
2. Ruth (Ruth 1:11-19)
3. David (I Sam. 18:22, 23)
4. Laban (Gen. 31:24)
5. Simon (Mark 1:30, 31)
6. Orpah (Ruth 1:14)
7. Jacob (Gen. 31:7)
8. Joseph (Gen. 41:45-50)
9. Samson (Judg. 15:5, 6)
10. Hobab (Num. 10:29)

JEALOUS PEOPLE

A. 10 (Esther 5:11-13)
B. 6 (Num. 12:1, 2)
C. 8 (Matt. 27:12, 18)
D. 2 (Gen. 26:12-14)
E. 7 (Gen. 21:9, 10)
F. 1 (I Sam. 18:6-9)
G. 9 (Gen. 37:3, 4)
H. 4 (Gen. 31:1)
I. 3 (Gen. 30:1)
J. 5 (Gen. 4:4, 5)

KIND PEOPLE

1. Boaz (Ruth 2:8, 9)
2. Israelites (Lev. 19:1, 2, 10)
3. Good Samaritan (Luke 10:30-35)

4. Publius (Acts 27:44; 28:7)
5. Onesiphorus (II Tim. 1:16)
6. Rebekah (Gen. 24:15-20)
7. David (II Sam. 9:3-7)
8. Dorcas (Acts 9:36, 39)
9. Shobi, Machir, Barzillai (II Sam. 17:27-29)
10. Shunammite woman (II Kings 4:8-10)

KINFOLK

1. Brother (Matt. 4:18)
2. Husband (Josh. 15:16, 17)
3. Cousin (Luke 1:36, 38)
4. Father-in-law (Exod. 18:1)
5. Mother (I Sam. 1:20)
6. Grandmother (II Tim. 1:5)
7. Uncle (Gen. 27:42, 43)
8. Daughter (II Sam. 11:3)
9. Nephew (Gen. 12:5)
10. Grandfather (Gen. 5:26-29)

KINGS

A. 7 (I Sam. 15:32, 33)
B. 9 (Deut. 3:11)
C. 6 (Dan. 4:33)
D. 5 (II Chron. 9:25)
E. 2 (I Sam. 15:26, 27)
F. 3 (II Kings 20:1-6)
G. 4 (Jer. 36:1, 21-23)
H. 10 (Dan. 5:1, 5)
I. 1 (II Chron. 16:12)
J. 8 (II Sam. 24:1, 2)

Answers

LEADERS

1. Joshua (Josh. 1:1, 2)
2. Peter (Acts 12:3-11)
3. David (I Sam. 22:1, 2)
4. Barak (Judg. 4:5-9)
5. Jesus (Mark 10:32)
6. Moses (Num. 20:3-5)
7. Ehud (Judg. 3:16-28)
8. Ezra (Ezra 7)
9. Gideon (Judg. 8:22, 23)

LIARS

1. Ananias and Sapphira (Acts 5:1-4)
2. Abraham and Isaac (Gen. 12:11-19; 20:2; 26:7-10)
3. Rahab (Josh. 2:1-6)
4. Gehazi (II Kings 5:20-27)
5. Peter (Matt. 26:69-74)
6. Sarah (Gen. 18:13-15)
7. David (I Sam. 21:1-3)
8. Cain (Gen. 4:8, 9)
9. Samson (Judg. 16:6-15)

MESSENGERS

1. Ehud (Judg. 3:20-22)
2. Jacob (Gen. 32:3-6)
3. Moses (Num. 20:14-17)
4. Ahaziah (II Kings 1:2)
5. Elisha (II Kings 5:9, 10)
6. Joshua (Josh. 7:21, 22)
7. Paul (II Cor. 12:7)
8. Saul (I Sam. 16:14 19)

9. Isaiah (Isa. 6:8)
10. Haman (Esther 3:12, 13)

MIRACLE WORKERS

A. 5 (Acts 3:2-8)
B. 7 (II Kings 20:8-11)
C. 6 (II Kings 6:5, 6)
D. 2 (John 2:1-11)
E. 9 (Josh. 10:12, 13)
F. 1 (Num. 20:7-11)
G. 4 (Judg. 15:14-16)
H. 3 (Exod. 7:10)
I. 8 (Acts 20:9-12)

MOTHERS

1. Eve (Gen. 3:20)
2. Hannah (I Sam. 1:22, 28)
3. Herodias (Matt. 14:6-8)
4. Zebedee's wife (Matt. 20:20, 21)
5. Rebekah (Gen. 27:6-19)
6. Jochebed (Exod. 2:1-9; 6:20)
7. Sarah (Gen. 17:15-17)
8. Hagar (Gen. 21:17, 21)

MURDERERS

1. Cain (Gen. 4:8)
2. Ehud (Judg. 3:15-22)
3. Athaliah (II Kings 11:1-3)
4. Rechab and Baanah (II Sam. 4:5-7)
5. Abner (II Sam. 2:18-23)
6. Jael (Judg. 5:24-27)

Answers

7. Hazael (II Kings 8:9-15)
8. Moses (Exod. 2:11-15)
9. Zimri (I Kings 16:9, 10)
10. Saul (I Sam. 19:10)

MUSICIANS

1. Asaph (I Chron. 16:5)
2. Miriam (Exod. 15:20)
3. Hezekiah
   (II Chron. 29:20, 25)
4. Jubal (Gen. 4:21)
5. David (I Sam. 16:16, 23)
6. Paul (I Cor. 13:1)
7. Captive Jews (Ps. 137:2, 3)
8. Four thousand
   (I Chron. 23:4, 5)
9. Solomon (I Kings 1:39, 40)
10. When the Ark was
    brought out of Abinadab's
    house (II Sam. 6:2, 5)

OBEDIENT PEOPLE

A. 8 (II Chron. 24:15, 16)
B. 9 (II Sam. 22:18-23)
C. 1 (I Kings 17:1-6)
D. 10 (II Chron. 14:1-7)
E. 7 (II Chron. 17:3-5)
F. 5 (Josh. 11:15, 16)
G. 4 (Gen. 6-7)
H. 2 (Gen. 22:16-18)
I. 6 (II Kings 18:1, 5-7)
J. 3 (Num. 14:24)

POOR PEOPLE

A. 6 (II Cor. 8:1-5)
B. 3 (Judg. 6:15)
C. 4 (Luke 15:14)
D. 2 (Luke 16:20, 21)
E. 1 (I Sam. 18:22, 23)
F. 7 (I Kings 17:12)
G. 5 (Neh. 5:1-5)

PRAYING PEOPLE

1. Elijah or Elias
   (James 5:17, 18)
2. Asa (II Chron. 14:8-11)
3. Samson (Judg. 15:18, 19)
4. David (II Sam. 7:29)
5. Hannah (I Sam. 1:10, 11)
6. Moses (Num. 12:10, 13)
7. Jacob (Gen. 32:9-11)
8. Manasseh
   (II Chron. 33:11-13)
9. Elisha (II Kings 6:18)
10. Manoah (Judg. 13:8)

PREACHERS

1. Paul (Acts 20:7-9)
2. Ecclesiastes
3. Jonah (Jonah 3:2-6)
4. Isaiah (Isa. 61:1)
5. 12 apostles
   (Matt. 10:27)
6. John the Baptist
   (Matt. 3:1)
7. Jesus (Luke 4:18-29)
8. Peter (Acts 2:1, 13-41)

Answers

9. Noah (II Peter 2:5)
10. Philip (Acts 8:5-13)

PRIESTS

1. Potipherah (Gen. 41:45)
2. Jehoiada (II Kings 12:9)
3. Eleazar (Num. 20:25-28)
4. Ezra (Ezra 7)
5. Eli (I Sam. 2:11, 12)
6. Ahimelech (I Sam. 21:1-9)
7. Abiathar (I Sam. 22:18-20)
8. Urijah (II Kings 16:10, 11)
9. Aaron (Exod. 28)
10. Caiaphas (John 11:49-53)

PROPHETS

1. Ezekiel (Ezek. 8:3)
2. Zechariah (Zech. 6:1-3)
3. Obadiah
4. Elisha (II Kings 2:22, 23)
5. Amos (Amos 7:14)
6. Jeremiah (Jer. 20:1, 2)
7. Isaiah (Isa. 38:21)
8. Jonah (Jonah 1:17)
9. Elijah (II Kings 2:11)
10. Daniel (Dan. 6:16)

SCRIBES

1. Jonathan (I Chron. 27:32)
2. Shebna (II Kings 19:1, 2)
3. Jesus (Matt. 23:1-33)
4. Shimshai (Ezra 4:8)
5. Shaphan (II Kings 22:8)

6. Zadok (Neh. 13:13)
7. Jeiel (II Chron. 26:11)
8. Baruch (Jer. 36:4)
9. Ezra (Neh. 8:1-4)
10. Haman (Esther 3:12, 13)

SINGERS

1. Paul and Silas (Acts 16:25)
2. Israelites (Exod. 32:4, 6, 18)
3. Solomon (I Kings 4:32)
4. Mount of Olives (Mark 14:26)
5. Josiah (II Chron. 35:23, 25)
6. Deborah and Barak (Judg. 5)
7. Jehoshaphat (II Chron. 20:17-21)
8. Moses (Exod. 15:1)
9. Cast lots (I Chron. 25:7, 8)

SOLDIERS

1. Cornelius (Acts 10)
2. Deborah (Judg. 4:4-10)
3. Abishai (II Sam. 21:15-17)
4. Vinegar (Luke 23:36)
5. Julius (Acts 27)
6. Uriah (II Sam. 11:14, 15)
7. Eliab (I Sam. 17:20, 28)
8. One year (Deut. 24:5)
9. Jonathan (I Sam. 14:4-13)
10. Eleazar (I Chron. 11:12-14)

Answers

SONS

A. 8 (Gen. 46-29)
B. 7 (Exod. 2:10)
C. 1 (I Sam. 20:34)
D. 9 (Luke 15:18, 19)
E. 2 (Gen. 25:28)
F. 4 (II Sam. 15:5-12)
G. 3 (I Tim. 1:2; II Tim. 1:2)
H. 6 (II Chron. 15:16)
I. 5 (Gen. 27:1-27)

THIEVES

1. Micah (Judg. 17:1, 2)
2. Barabbas (Matt. 27:11-26)
3. Rachel (Gen. 31:19)
4. Achan (Josh. 7:20, 21)
5. Five (Judg. 18:17, 18)
6. Shishak (I Kings 14:25, 26)
7. Men of Shechem (Judg. 9:25)
8. Judas Iscariot (John 12:4-6)
9. Paul (II Cor. 11:8)
10. Benjamin (Gen. 44:1-12)

TRAVELERS

1. Elisha (II Kings 2:2-7)
2. Ruth (Ruth 1:18, 19)
3. Barnabas (Acts 13:2-4)
4. Jesus (Luke 24:13-15)
5. Jacob (Gen. 46:2-27)
6. Joseph (Matt. 2:19-23)
7. Abram and Lot (Gen. 12:1-5)
8. Jesus' 12 disciples (Luke 9:1-3)
9. Rebekah (Gen. 24:58-61)
10. Ten (Gen. 42:2, 3)

WEALTHY PEOPLE

A. 6 (II Chron. 32:27)
B. 8 (I Kings 10:23)
C. 4 (Matt. 19:21, 22)
D. 1 (Luke 19:2)
E. 7 (Gen. 13:2)
F. 5 (Esther 1:1, 4)
G. 2 (II Chron. 17:3-5)
H. 3 (I Sam. 25:2-11)

WIVES

A. 8 (Judg. 1:12, 13)
B. 3 (Gen. 24:51-66)
C. 1 (Esther 1:3, 11, 12)
D. 6 (Gen. 3:1-6, 17)
E. 7 (Acts 5:1-10)
F. 5 (Esther 5:14)
G. 4 (I Sam. 25:14-19)
H. 2 (I Kings 21:7)

GLOBE

GLOBE DIGEST SERIES

If you enjoyed this book...
then you'll want to order these other
Globe Digest favorites!

120   Heal Yourself

123   650 Home Remedies

205   Getting Organized

206   Women's Intimate Secrets

207   Why Do Women Get
        the Blues

210   Protect Yourself
        From Crime

306   How to Read Palms

402   Cat Life

GETTING ORGANIZED!
TIPS TO SAVE YOU TIME & MONEY

- KITCHEN
- CLOSETS
- SHOPPING
- MONEY
- GARDEN
- CHILDREN
- STORAGE
- CLOTHES
- COOKING
- GUESTS
- PAPERS
- TOOLS
- CLEANING
- TRAVEL
- GARAGE

**Mail to: Globe Digest Series, P.O. Box 114,
Rouses Point, NY 12979-0114**

Please check the desired title numbers below:

☐ 120   ☐ 207
☐ 123   ☐ 210
☐ 205   ☐ 306
☐ 206   ☐ 402

YES! Please send me the titles I've checked – each at $2.29 ($2.79 in Canada) plus .95¢ each for shipping & handling. With my order of 3 or more titles, I save all shipping & handling costs.

D36

Name_____
PLEASE PRINT

Address_____

City_____ St_____ Zip_____

PLEASE COMPLETE

U.S. Only: I enclose total of $3.24 for each of ____titles equaling $_____
(if ordering 3 or more titles, enclose only $2.29 for each)

Canadian Only: I enclose total of $3.74 for each of ____titles equaling $_____
(if ordering 3 or more titles, enclose only $2.79 for each)

Please allow 4 to 8 weeks for your order to arrive.